Cow takes a bow
and other tales

Russell Punter, Lesley Sims
& Mairi Mackinnon

Illustrated by Fred Blunt

Contents

About phonics

Phonics is a method of teaching reading used extensively in today's schools. At its heart is an emphasis on identifying the *sounds* of letters, or combinations of letters, that are then put together to make words. These sounds are known as phonemes.

Starting to read

Learning to read is an important milestone for any child. The process can begin well before children start to learn letters and put them together to read words. The sooner children can discover books and enjoy stories and language, the better they will be prepared for reading themselves, first with the help of an adult and then independently.

You can find out more about phonics on the Usborne Very First Reading website, **www.usborne.com/veryfirstreading** (US readers go to **www.veryfirstreading.com**). Click on the **Parents** tab at the top of the page, then scroll down and click on **About synthetic phonics**.

Phonemic awareness

An important early stage in pre-reading and early reading is developing phonemic awareness: that is, listening out for the sounds within words. Rhymes, rhyming stories and alliteration are excellent ways of encouraging this.

In the following stories, your child will soon identify common sounds, such as the *ow* in **cow**; the *ai* in **snail**; the *ee* in **bee**; the *a* in **ants**; the *o* in **croc** and the *ow* as in **crow**. Each story has lots of fun rhymes to look out for, and there are puzzles at the end of the book for further practice.

Hearing your child read

If your child is reading a story to you, don't rush to correct mistakes, but be ready to prompt or guide if he or she is struggling. Above all, do give plenty of praise and encouragement.

Cow takes a bow

Today the circus is in town.

CIRCUS

Brown Cow sets out
to track it down.

"I'd like a seat, please," says Brown Cow.

Here comes the boss.
Cow sees him frown.

13

"I'll help," says Cow.

"Just show me how."

Cow slips and trips.

She tries some tricks...

...but drops the pies,

and spills the bricks.

17

Her tricycle just
spins around.

Her trumpet
makes a silly sound.

Her juggling balls all hit the ground.

Her hat flies off.

Her pants fall down.

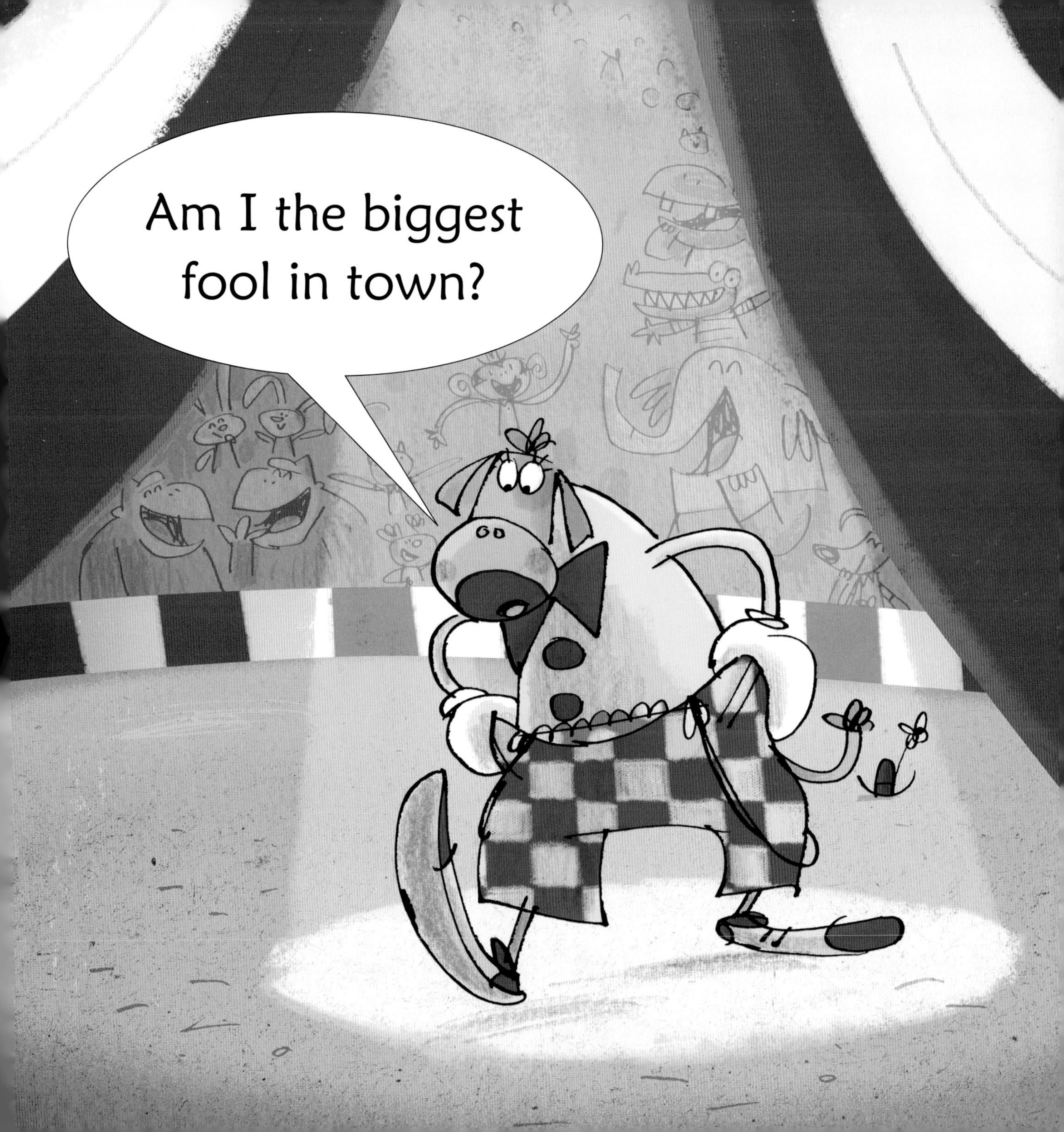
Am I the biggest fool in town?

"It's all gone wrong!"
Brown Cow flops down.

Now she's the one who wears a frown.

"I'm sorry I messed up!" howls Cow.

"No, wait!"
the boss shouts.

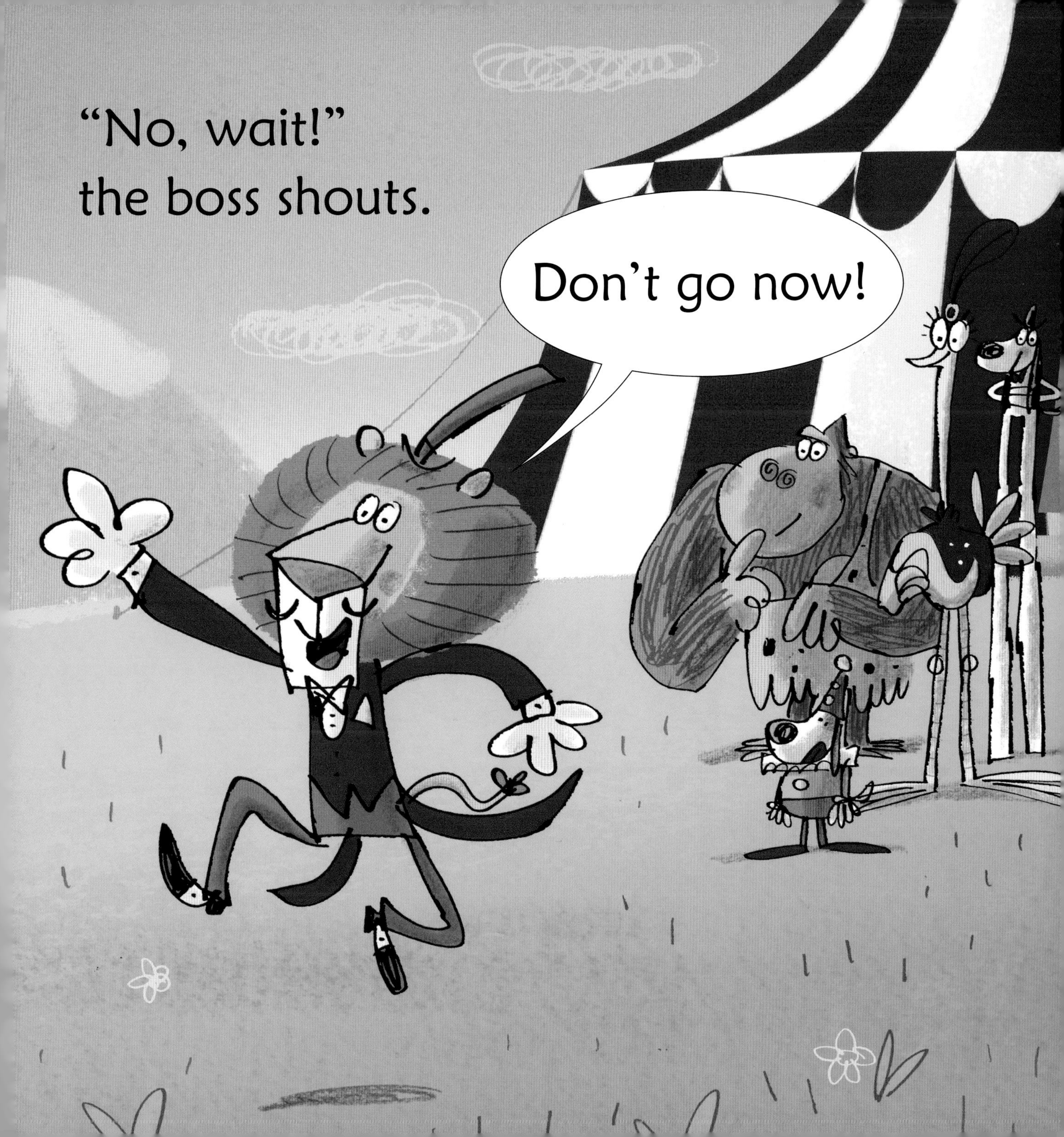

"Listen!" he says.

The crowd shouts, "Wow!"

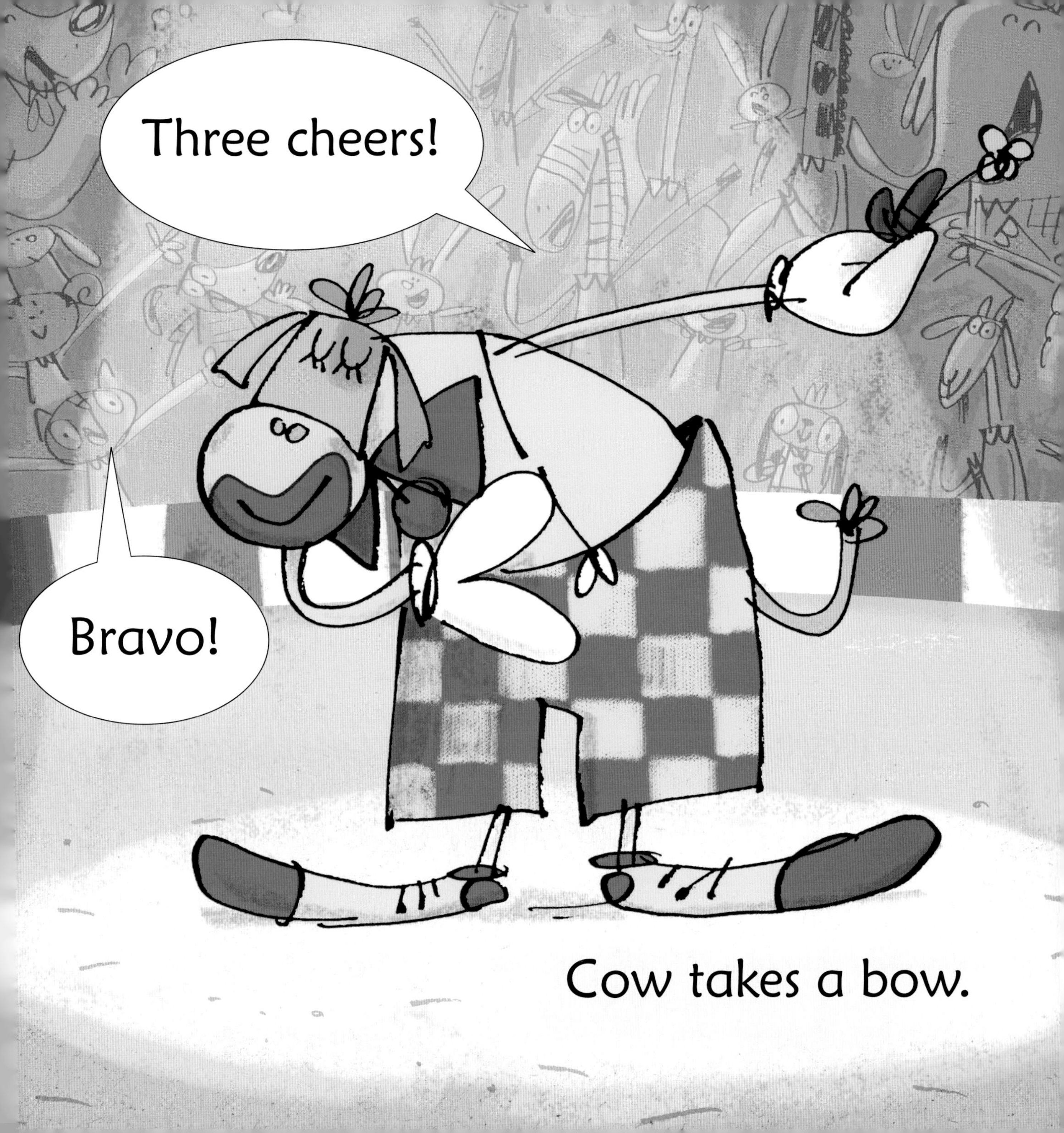

Cow takes a bow.

Snail brings the mail

Hooray for Snail! He brings the mail.

Day in, day out, he will not fail.

A box
for Fox,

and three
for Bee.

From dawn to dusk, Snail's on the go.

He does work hard, but he's so slow.

His friends may
have to wait all day.

"Poor Snail. He does his best," they say.

One morning, things go wrong for Snail.

He wakes up late.

He drops the mail.

It starts to rain. It starts to hail.

Snail won't give up.

I must
not fail.

The cold wind blows – it's quite a gale.

The sky turns dark,

and Snail turns pale.

The road is flooded.
Bad luck, Snail.

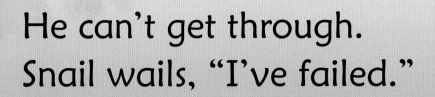

He can't get through.
Snail wails, "I've failed."

But look! A tractor – up for sale!

The deal is done. Now watch Snail go!

He won't get stuck in rain or snow.

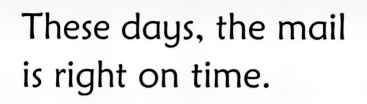 These days, the mail
is right on time.

And Snail gets through,

come rain or shine.

Bee makes tea

Meet Bee.

Bee lives
beside the sea.

Today she's all a-flutter, for it's Queen Bee's birthday tea.

Bee buzzes home
and starts to bake.

Soon her rooms fill up with cake.

Chocolate cheesecakes on the chairs...

Cherry cupcakes
up the stairs...

Pies piled high with
plums and pears.

Ant runs in and grins with glee.
"You're making tea!"

For my
Queen Bee.

"Her birthday tea is by the sea."

They stack up cups and fill the pot.
Bee starts to frown. It looks a lot.

"Oh Ant, how will I carry that?"
"Wait there," says Ant.

I'll soon
be back.

He finds his friends and lines them up.

They carry cakes and plates and cups.

Two take the milk.
Three take the pot.

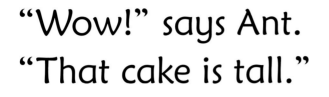

"Wow!" says Ant.
"That cake is tall."

"Speed up!" shouts Ant.
"Move that cake faster."

Then one ant slips and trips...
Disaster!

"Oh no!" Bee cries.
She sobs and sighs.

That *was* my Queen Bee's big surprise.

"The Queen will be so mad with me.
She'll say that I'm a bad, bad bee."

"Collect it all," Ant tells his team.
"Now quick, Bee!
Whip some buttercream."

"You need to use the cream like glue...
See? Stuck together, good as new."

The Queen Bee gasps and laughs, "Hee, hee! A special cake that looks like me?"

"Thank you for my birthday tea!"

Underpants for ants

Nan sells fancy fans and lamps,

hand bells,

clam shells,

pans and stamps.

But customers just stay away.

And so she sits and knits all day.

One cold night, Nan lights a candle,

and grabs a small pan by the handle.

But as she pours soup from a can...

a gang of ants leaps from the pan.

“We sneaked in from the freezing storm.”

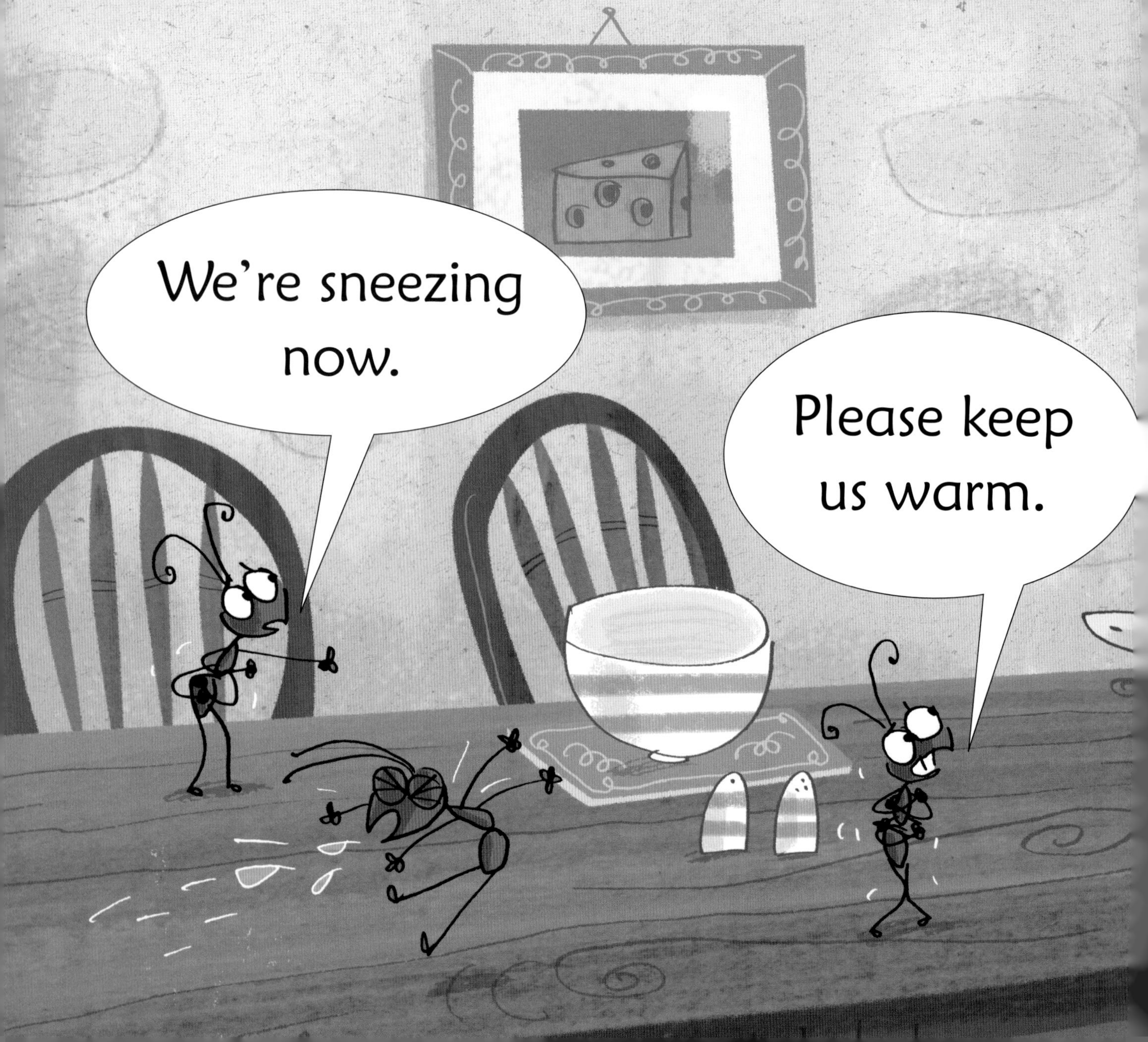

"Hot water bottles
would be nice."

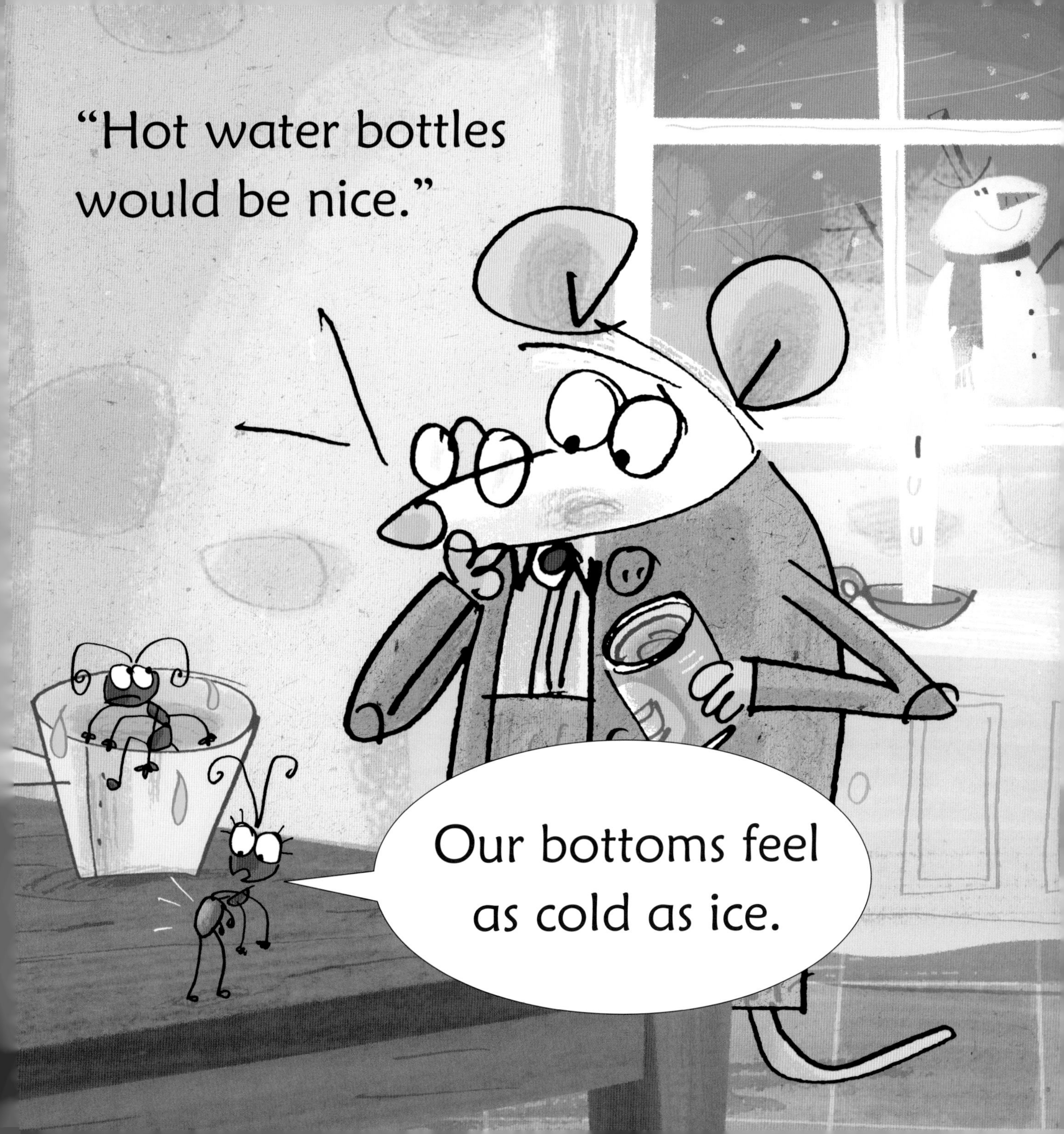

"I can help you," Nan declares.

"I have yards of yarn to spare.

I'll knit you something warm to wear."

Nan's whiskers twitch.
Her needles click.

"Handmade underpants!"
"How grand."

Soon bugs are hopping up the hill.

Nan's shop is full, and so's her till.

Nan gets a snug hug from the ants.

"Thanks for our wonderful underpants!"

Croc gets a shock

Knock knock. "Who's there?"

"Hey, wake up, Croc!"

"You've overslept – it's ten o'clock!"

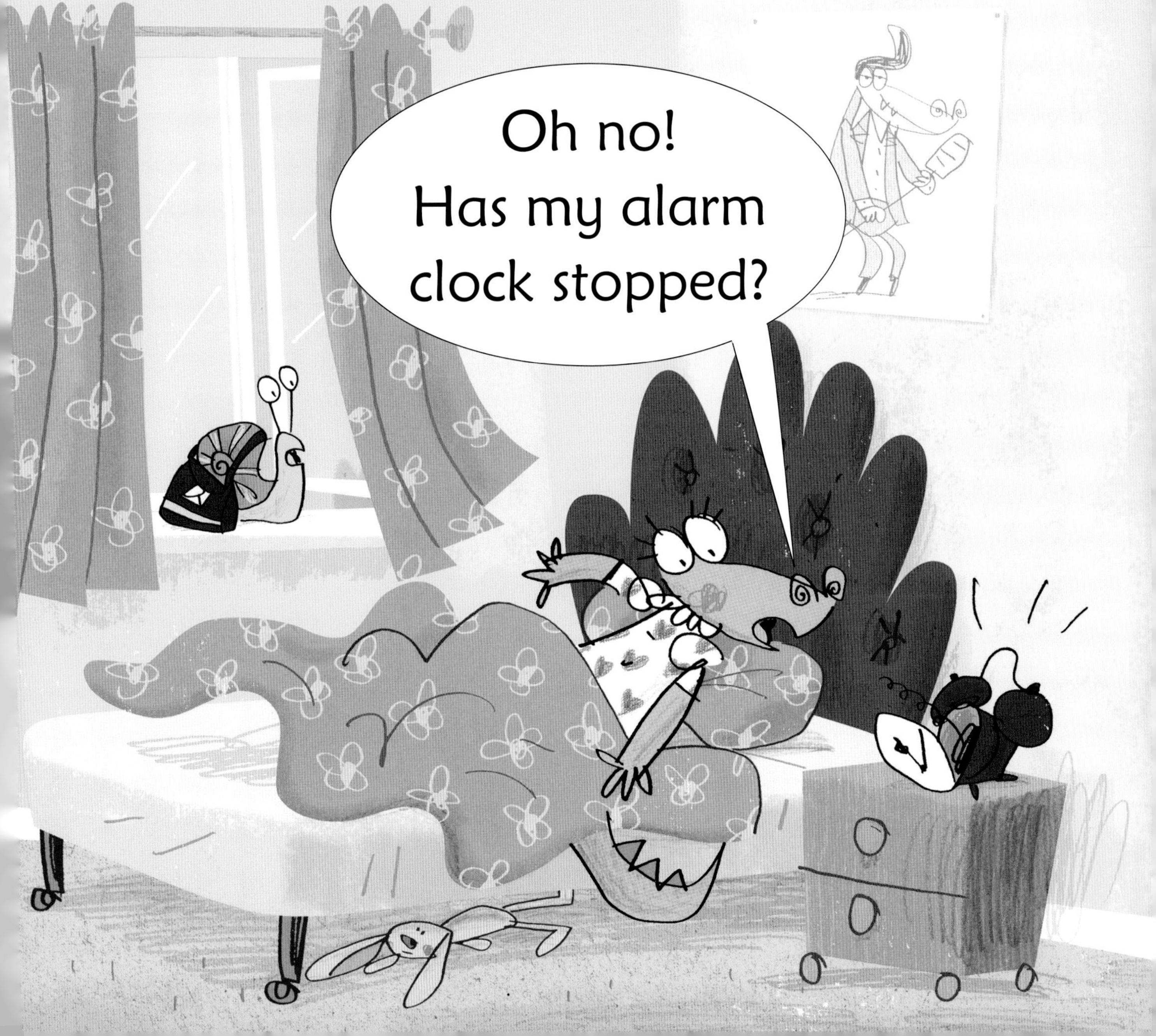

"I'm late! And there's so much to do –

I need new shoes, a new bag too.
I'm due at The Zoo at twenty to two."

Croc gulps her breakfast,

grabs her stuff.

She runs, but she's not quick enough.
"I've missed the bus!" She's out of puff.

Hic

Now Croc's in town. "It can't be true!"
The shoe store door says CLOSED TILL 2.

She sighs. "These boots will have to do."

It's party time! The Zoo looks fine.
The lions and rhinos wait in line.

Happy Birthday Croc!

The hippos hold a birthday sign.
But where is Croc?

"We'll have to wait. She's always late."

Happy Birthday Croc!

"At last! Come on, let's celebrate!"

Croc swallows quickly.
"What's up, Croc?"

"Unwrap your presents, Croc."
Croc picks a box...

...and gets a shock.
"CUCKOO! CUCKOO!"

"My gosh! I almost dropped the box."

"You've never seen a cuckoo clock?"

"Hey, Croc! Guess what?
Your hiccups have stopped!"

"It was the shock."

"It's a tip-top tick-tock cuckoo clock!"

Crow in the snow

Crow is flying over snow.

He spies some paw prints far below.

"Ho, ho," says Crow
and swoops down low.

"I think I'll follow where they go."

Then – five fine snowmen,
side by side.

Ho, ho!
I know...

Crow starts hopping to and fro.

He picks up sticks,
    some stones and cones...

And look –
a crow made out of snow.

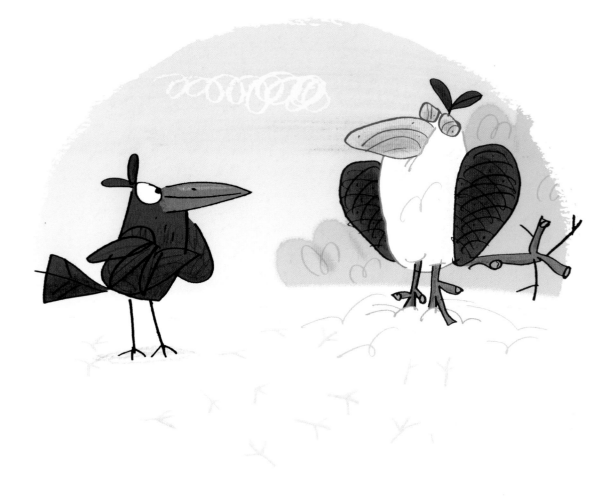

Crow blinks and sees the
trail goes on. "What next?"
he thinks and trots along.

He spots a red
sled by a gate,

a yellow
hat,

a fallen
skate.

The trail leads to...

...a frozen lake.

Creak!

Mice and voles
and Mole are skating.

"Oh no!" cries Crow.
"The ice is breaking."

Crack!

"Help!" calls Mole. "I'm falling in.
I'm all cold and I can't swim."

129

Crow flies fast.

He leaves the lake.
In seconds, he's flown past the gate.

He spies the snowmen, dives down low, grabs a scarf and back he goes.

With one last heave, cold Mole is free.
He sits and shivers by a tree.

"Let me get the sled," says Crow...

and soon he's giving Mole a tow.

Now all are warm and safe and snug.
Mole gives a grin and lifts his mug.

"A toast," he says. "A toast to Crow. He's the hero of the snow!"

Puzzles

Puzzle 1

Can you find the words that rhyme?

frown	click	ball
call	tock	thick
clock	fall	clown
tick	down	sock

Puzzle 2

One word is wrong in this speech bubble.
What should it be?

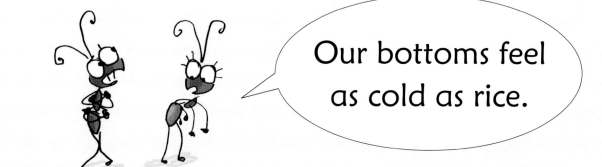

Our bottoms feel
as cold as rice.

Puzzle 3

Can you point to these things in the picture?
One is missing. What is it?

hail　　　　　shell　　　　　letter

bee

bag

tree

ant

Puzzle 4

Choose the right word for each sentence.

1. Snail must not ....

| pail | tail | fail |

2. Bee .... a cake.

| wakes | rakes | bakes |

3. .... runs for the bus.

| Croc | rock | lock |

4. The ants are ....

| fold | cold | hold |

Puzzle 5

Which sentence fits each picture best?

1.

The pot is hot.
That looks a lot.

2.

No time now!
Cow takes a bow.

3.

Oh no – I'm late!
Hurray. I'm great.

4.

Crow slips in snow.
Crow swoops low.

Answers to puzzles

Puzzle 1

frown   →   down   →   clown

call   →   fall   →   ball

clock   →   tock   →   sock

tick   →   click   →   thick

Puzzle 2

Our bottoms feel as cold as <u>ice</u>.

Puzzle 3

The bee is missing.

(You could point to any hailstone or tree.)

shell

letter

bag

tree

hail

ant

Puzzle 4

1. Snail must not <u>fail</u>.

2. Bee <u>bakes</u> a cake.

3. <u>Croc</u> runs for the bus.

4. The ants are <u>cold</u>.

Puzzle 5

1. That looks a lot.

2. Cow takes a bow.

3. Oh no – I'm late!

4. Crow swoops low.

Edited by Jenny Tyler, Lesley Sims and Mairi Mackinnon
Designed by Caroline Spatz and Sam Chandler

Reading consultants: Alison Kelly and Anne Washtell

This edition first published in 2015 by Usborne Publishing Ltd., Usborne House, 83-85 Saffron Hill, London EC1N 8RT, England. www.usborne.com Copyright © 2015, 2014, 2013 Usborne Publishing Ltd.